FUZZY'S FEELINGS

Written and Illustrated by LEFD Designs

This is Fuzzy. Fuzzy has lots of feelings. Fuzzy's colors change all the time depending on how Fuzzy is feeling. Fuzzy's colors can be like a rainbow on some days.

Right now, Fuzzy is yellow. Fuzzy says, "I am feeling
HAPPY."

Fuzzy is smiling and laughing. Fuzzy is playing with
his favorite toy. Fuzzy is happy.

HAPPY

Fuzzy says being happy feels like a ball of sunshine in your belly, all warm and tingly.

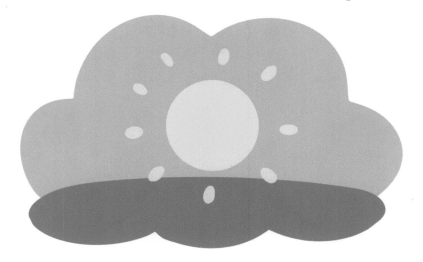

So Fuzzy spreads happiness by smiling and being kind to others. That way others can feel happy too!

Fuzzy says, "I am feeling happy, but sometimes my feelings change, and that's okay."

Fuzzy's color begins to change. Right now, Fuzzy is purple. Fuzzy says, "I am feeling SCARED."

Fuzzy's eyes are wide, his heart is pounding and he is frozen in place. His mouth is dry and his palms are sweating. Fuzzy had a nightmare. Fuzzy is scared.

SCARED

Fuzzy says being scared feels like you're a tiny little mouse and a big lion is roaring at you.

So Fuzzy takes 5 deep breaths and fills his belly with air, just like a balloon. Fuzzy finds something to cuddle.

Fuzzy says, "I was feeling scared, but soon I will be okay."

Fuzzy's color begins to change. Right now, Fuzzy is red. Fuzzy says, "I am feeling ANGRY."

Fuzzy's fists are clenched, his shoulders are tight, his heart is pounding and he is talking louder. Fuzzy's sister broke his toy. Fuzzy is angry.

ANGRY

Fuzzy says being angry feels like you're a bubbling hot volcano ready to explode.

So Fuzzy takes 5 deep breaths and fills his belly with air, just like a balloon. He must not hurt anyone or anything with mean words or actions. Fuzzy takes a 5 minute time-out. He walks away to do something he enjoys, until those angry feelings fade away and he can use calm words.

Fuzzy says, "I was feeling angry, but soon I will be okay."

Fuzzy's color begins to change. Right now, Fuzzy is blue. Fuzzy says, "I am feeling SAD."

Fuzzy's shoulders are slumped, his lips are quivering and he has tears welling up. Fuzzy doesn't have anyone to play with. Fuzzy is sad.

SAD

Fuzzy says being sad feels like there's a big, dark, stormy rain cloud over your head.

So Fuzzy takes 5 deep breaths and fills his belly with air, just like a balloon. Fuzzy asks for help from a grown-up. Sometimes all you need to do is talk to someone you trust and you will start to feel better.

Fuzzy says, "I was feeling sad, but soon I will be okay."

Fuzzy's color begins to change. Right now, Fuzzy is grey. Fuzzy says, "I am feeling ANXIOUS."

Fuzzy's body is shaking, his tummy is queasy and he is breathing quickly. His mind keeps telling him that something bad will happen. Fuzzy is worried about getting sick. Fuzzy is anxious.

ANXIOUS

Fuzzy says being anxious feels like your thoughts are racing around your head and there are butterflies fluttering in your tummy.

So Fuzzy takes 5 deep breaths and fills his belly with air, just like a balloon. Fuzzy tells himself that the feeling will pass and he will be okay. Fuzzy looks around and counts 5 things he can see, hear, smell, taste and feel.

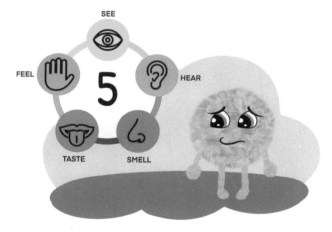

Fuzzy says, "I was feeling anxious, but soon I will be okay."

Fuzzy's color begins to change. Right now, Fuzzy is green. Fuzzy says, "I am feeling JEALOUS."

Fuzzy is frowning and his lips are in a straight line. His arms are crossed. Fuzzy's friend won a medal and he is getting all the attention. Fuzzy is jealous.

JEALOUS

Fuzzy says being jealous feels like you're comparing yourself to someone else and wondering why you can't have what they have.

So Fuzzy takes 5 deep breaths and fills his belly with air, just like a balloon. Fuzzy tells himself that he doesn't need to be jealous. Fuzzy has his own strengths that he is good at so he focuses on being the best version of himself.

Fuzzy says, "I was feeling jealous, but soon I will be okay."

Fuzzy's color begins to change. Right now, Fuzzy is pink. Fuzzy says, "I am feeling EMBARRASSED."

Fuzzy's cheeks are hot and flushed and he begins to sweat. Fuzzy tripped over and missed the ball when he tried to kick it. Fuzzy's friends laughed at him. Fuzzy is embarrassed.

EMBARRASSED

Fuzzy says being embarrassed feels like everyone is staring at you and all you want to do is run and hide.

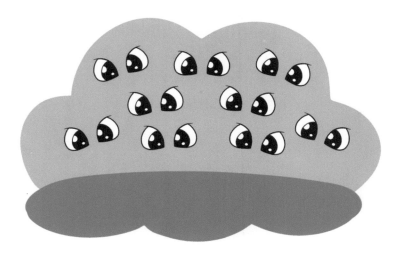

So Fuzzy takes 5 deep breaths and fills his belly with air, just like a balloon. Fuzzy tells himself that it's okay to make mistakes. Fuzzy shows resilience and tries again.

Fuzzy says, "I was feeling embarrassed, but soon I will be okay."

Fuzzy's color begins to change. Right now, Fuzzy is orange. Fuzzy says, "I am feeling EMPATHY."

Fuzzy sees his sister with her shoulders slumped, her lips quivering and tears welling up in her eyes. She is the color blue. Fuzzy thinks about how she is feeling and puts himself in her shoes. Fuzzy shows empathy.

EMPATHY

Fuzzy looked at his sister and saw the way her facial expression and body language were showing sadness. She must be sad! Fuzzy knew what it was like to feel sad when he had no one to play with. Even though Fuzzy wasn't feeling sad right now, he put himself in her shoes and understood how she was feeling.

So Fuzzy told his sister to take 5 deep breaths and fill her belly with air, just like a balloon. Fuzzy put a comforting arm around her and gave his sister a toy to help her feel better. Fuzzy showed the feeling of empathy. He was able to understand how someone else was feeling and respond. Now Fuzzy finally understood all those feelings and he could see what they might look like.

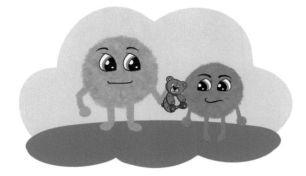

Fuzzy says, "My sister was feeling sad, so I helped her feel better by showing empathy."

Our colors can change all the time and some days we might go through every color of the rainbow! But now that we know all these different feelings, we can work through them.

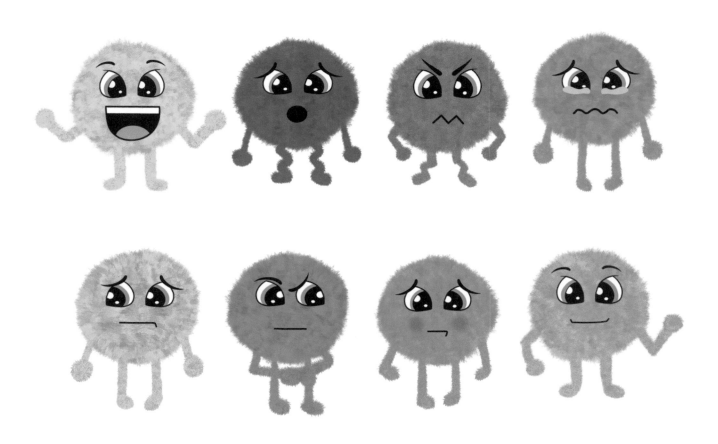

Fuzzy says, "I understand that we all have different feelings for different reasons and that's okay."

CPSIA information can be obtained
at www.ICGtesting.com
Printed in the USA
BVHW021827030621
608542BV00014B/136